"Bubblegum"

The Lurve Guide

An essential "Bubblegum" guide

Ged Backland and Phil Renshaw

SCHOLASTIC

With thanx to
Jez Spencer, Ben Whittington,
Keith Auty and all at Carlton Cards

The Lurve Guide

The Essential Guide to the Big L Word

Welcome to the Bubblegum Lurve Guide, the essential handbook to lurve and all that stuff. Inside you'll find out what love has in store for you and your mates in Mystic Mog's fun lovin' lurve scopes. So check out whether you're a nicey Pisces or a scarey Aries. Find out about all the cool Bubblegum Lurve crew like Snog Monster and Secret Admirer in their character profiles. Fancy cooking up a special lurve feed? Then get a load of the crazy recipes and whip up some dreams on toast for that spesh bod. All in all it's the big Bubblegum take on the L word.

Enjoy!

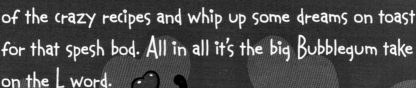

Hug

Hug likes a big fat one
if it's him you want to please
Stretch out your arms, wrap them around
and give him a flippin' big squeeze!

Hug is so loving that he'll hug you any where, any time, any place. He feels it's his duty to hug everyone he sees, so don't be surprised to get a great big squeeze if you ever bump into him, wherever you happen to be.

Most Likely to say...

This hug is on me

Most likely to be...

At an international hug festival

Fave Colour

'Squeeze me' purple

Q Here 4 Hugz

What Hug likes to do
is squeeze you 'til you go blue

Snog Monster

Snog Monster loves a kiss
she showers them all over the place
So if you're about, you'd better watch out
she'll plant 'em all over your face!

Snog monster just loves a kiss. It's a wonder that she hasn't worn her lips out! She's an absolute terror when it comes to planting kisses on you when you're least expecting it. At Crimbo she buys mistletoe by the sack load and has an absolute ball. So you'd better watch out when Snog Monster's about!

Most likely to be...

Puckering up to pounce

Most likely to say...

Gizza kiss

Fave Colour

Lipstick Pink

What Snog monster will always seek
is a quick peck on your cheek

Kitten

Kitten is so gorgeous
dizzy and cute you could say
An utterly pretty, cute little Kitty
and purrfect in every way

Kitten is the dahling of the Bubblegum Lurve crew. Her trademark fun fur ears and leopard skin boots make her stand out in any crowd. When Kitten is around you'll always find more than a few Cool Cats in her company.

Most Likely to say...

Purrrrrrrr...Purrrrrrrrrr...

Most likely to be...

Surrounded by Cool Cats

Fave Colour

Smooth Blue

With this lass the boys are smitten
'Cos she's such an adorable Kitten

Fit Fella

He's proper gorge, he's just so fine
perfection – he is it
All the girls just swoon and swirl
over this fella who is proper fit!

Fit Fella is fit as flippin' anything. He could be the lead singer of any boy band, 'cos he's got the looks, the style and the attitude that says... "I'm cooler than a penguin's pants". All the girls love him and even mums think he's a 'nice boy'.

Most likely to be...

Surrounded by sacks of cards on Valentine's Day

Most likely to say...

Hello Girls

Fave Colour

Velvet Red

Fit Fella is really ace,
a pretty boy with a gorgepot face

Love Docta'

Crazy Love Docta's a nutter
in fact he's as mad as cheese
Its hard to tell if you're under his spell
but you'll know if you're weak at the knees

Love Docta is a mad top-hatted geezer full of crazy fun. Watch out if he's around because he's got a big bag choc full of love spells that will turn your legs to jelly and put a whole swarm of butterflies in your belly.

Most Likely to say...

Look into my eyes

Most likely to be...

Prescribing love potions and inflicting wicked crushes

Fave Colour

Shocking magenta

Love Docta is a crazy guy
You'll be under his spell in the blink of an eye

Animal

Animal is just so cute
a big ball of bright blue fluff
The girls all think he's really sweet
and hug him 'til he's had enuff!

Animal is possibly the cutest of the Bubblegum Lurve crew. He's just so cuddly that you can't resist wanting to give him the most ginormous humungous squeeze. Everyone wants him to be their own pet hug.

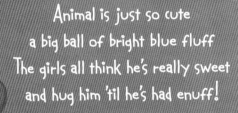

Most likely to be...

In the grip of a vice-like hug

Most likely to say...

One hug at a time, ladies, please

Fave Colour

Crushed Cranberry

Animal's dead easy to please,
Just give him a great big squeeze!

Horny Devil

He's always very cheeky
his cheek reaches another level
He's full of fun – he's number one
a proper little devil

Horny Devil is by far the cheekiest of the Bubblegum Lurve crew. Always up to some devilish mischief, he's the real joker in the pack. He'll tease all the girls with his trident then go home and make some toast on it by the fire.

Most likely to be...

Up to mischief or playing tricks on the girls

Most likely to say...

I'm a proper little Devil, I am!

Fave Colour

Deep Devilish Red

Horny Devil is full of fun,
for devilish fun he's number one!

Top Kisser

He's always right on target
with a smacker that never misses
He gives it large, 'cos he's in charge
with his super smashing kisses

Top Kisser is just that. He loves to give kisses like they're going out of style, in fact it's surprising that he hasn't worn his lips out by now. He's a really nice bod though and will often commit random acts of kindness doing anything for anyone (in exchange for a peck on the cheek of course).

Most likely to be...

Blowing kisses to everyone

Most likely to say...

Giz a kiss

Fave Colour

Kissing Pink

Top Kisser's a bod you can't miss,
when he meets you, he'll give you a kiss

Mr Love Pants

He's proper mad and crazy
he's got love for us all
It's easy to see, I'm sure you'll agree
he's havin' a flippin' ball!

Mr Love Pants is a great bod. Everyone loves him and he loves everyone. He wears his heart on his sleeve – well he carries it in his hand actually. He's always smiling and you can recognise him by his trademark mad (and sad) Y-fronts.

Most Likely to say...
Look at my undies!

Most likely to be...
On everyone's Valentine's Day card list

Fave Colour
Blue and red (together)

Mr Love Pants is proper mad
but his undies are proper sad!

Stunna

Stunna stops people in their tracks
as they walk along the street
'Cos she's so utterly gorgeous
from her head to her boogaloo feet!

A 100 per cent gorgepot, Stunna is the envy of all the Bubblegum gals and the dahling of all the Bubblegum boys, who get a serious case of jelly legs whenever she's about. This proper babe causes mega havoc every time she pops out to the shops.

Most likely to be...
Surrounded by boys

Most likely to say...
No, you can't have a kiss

Fave Colour
Candy Pink

Stunna is a proper dolly
she sends every bloke right off his trolley!

Secret Admirer

In big hat and dark glasses
just who could they be?
They lurk deep in the shadows
sending cards to you and me!

Secret likes to keep his or her identity top secret, wearing dark glasses to avoid
being recognised. After all if we knew who he or she was then it wouldn't be
half so much fun, would it?

Most Likely to say...

Sssssssh!

Most likely to be...

Sneaking off to post a secret love note

Fave Colour

Darkest Black

Secret Admirer's identity is hush hush
but they might tell you at a push

Who luvs who in the Bubblegum crew?

Unravel the boot laces to find out which member of the Bubblegum crew has got a crush on who...

Mystic Mog's Lurvescopes

Aries 21st March – 20th April

Baaaaaaa

Aries are full of energy
always buzzin' around
Aries are lovely people
proper kind and sound

If you're an Aries, then this means you are a fire sign.
So your characteristics include loving to talk a lot, being
really, totally and utterly enthusiastic about things
(even when it's boring stuff like tidying up!), being mega
competitive (you always want to win even if it's to be
first in the bloomin' chip shop queue) and independent
(you prefer to do things without anyone's help!).

Perfect Boy/Girlfriend

Leo (both big egos)
Sagittarius (both have extravagant taste!)
Might be Ok with... Taurus, Gemini, Aquarius, Pisces
50/50 chance with... Virgo, Scorpio
No bloomin' chance with... Cancer, Libra, Capricorn, Aries

Gem stone   Diamond

Bubblegum Crew who are Arians

Boy
Racer

Loopy Lass

Shoe
Queen

Taurus 21st April - 20th May

Taurians are so warm hearted
patient, loving and kind
A better bud or soulmate
you could never find

If you're a Taurus, then you are an Earth sign.
This means that you're warm hearted and will listen
to anyone's problems (and dish out good advice).
So your characteristics include being calm (even when
things are going flippin' mental all around) and being loyal
(you're the bestest bud anyone could ever wish for).
However, you can be a little stubborn and once you've
made up your mind that's flippin' well it!

Perfect Boy / Girlfriend

Virgo (love at first sight)
Capricorn (both straight forward and uncomplicated!)
Might be Ok with... Taurus, Pisces, Aries, Gemini, Cancer
50/50 chance with... Libra, Sagittarius
No bloomin' chance with Aquarius, Leo, Scorpio

Gem stone   Emerald

Bubblegum Crew
who are Taurians

Diamond
Geezer

Designer
Diva

£300

Gemini 21st May – 20th June

Geminis are so clever
and always on the go
If you need the answer to a problem
Geminis are the bods to know

If you're a Gemini, then this means you are an air sign. So your characteristics include being a proper brainbox, (you probably know all the answers on Who Wants To Be A Millionaire), always on the go (you never stop even when eating) and you love solving problems and undertaking tasks that would leave other star signs feeling whacked out.

Perfect Boy / Girlfriend
Libra (both air signs with tons of brains)
Aquarius (both get along famously)
Might be Ok with... Taurus, Cancer, Leo, Aries
50/50 chance with... Scorpio, Capricorn
No bloomin' chance with... Virgo, Sagittarius, Pisces

Gem stone Agate

Bubblegum Crew
who are Geminis

Clever Clogs

Smile

Cancer 21st June – 20th July

Cancerians are caring
they lend everyone an ear
If you're upset you can always be sure
a Cancerian's big hug is near

If you're a Cancerian, then this means you are a water sign. So your characteristics include being very emotional (you'll even blub at the adverts), very sentimental (you love giving and receiving little gifts) and you're a bit moody (you'll throw a blubby hissy-fit at the drop of a hat).

Perfect Boy / Girlfriend
Scorpio (both admire each other's qualities)
Pisces (make a proper sensitive couple)
Might be Ok with... Taurus, Gemini, Leo, Virgo
50/50 chance with... Sagittarius, Aquarius
No bloomin' chance with... Libra, Capricorn, Aries, Cancer

Gem stone   Moonstone

Bubblegum Crew
who are Cancerians

Hug

Groovy Chick

Hunny Bunny

Leo 21st July - 21st August

Leos are very organised
yet love tons of fun
This makes lovely Leos
fun bods number one

If you're a Leo, then this means you are a fire sign.
So your characteristics include being proper organised
(your bedroom is spotless, you file bloomin' everything),
you are creative (we've seen your hair), but you
can be a little bossy boots at times (a right little general!).

Perfect Boy / Girlfriend
Sagittarius (both fun loving)
Aries (you two are the superstars of the zodiac)
Might be Ok with... Virgo, Cancer, Libra, Gemini
50/50 chance with... Pisces, Capricorn, Leo
No bloomin' chance with... Scorpio, Taurus, Aquarius

Gem stone Ruby

Bubblegum Crew
who are Leos

Funk Soul
Brother

Cool
Dude

Nutty
Tart

Virgo 22nd August - 22nd September

Virgos are very modest
and oh so efficient too
This makes lovely Virgos
good friends, trusted and true!

If you're a Virgo, then this means you are an earth sign.
So your characteristics include being proper efficient
(you're the one to organise the mega day out),
you are modest (gorgeous, but you don't know it)
but you do like to have a little whinge about things
(this coffee is cold!).

Perfect Boy / Girlfriend

Capricorn (both admire each other's finely-tuned minds)
Taurus (both are devoted to each other)
Might be Ok with... Leo, Cancer, Libra
50/50 chance with... Aries, Aquarius
No bloomin' chance with... Pisces, Gemini

Gem stone Sardonyx

Bubblegum Crew
who are Virgos

Gym
Queen

100% Bad

Libra 23rd September – 22nd October

Librans like to keep the peace
and are soft and kind and gentle
But when they let their hair down
they can be flippin' mental!

If you're a Libran, then this means you are an air sign.
So your characteristics include being the peace keeper
(you're the one to to sort out fights and squabbles),
you are sociable (always surrounded by tons of people),
although you are prone to changing your mind (more often
than your sister changes outfits on a Saturday night).

Perfect Boy / Girlfriend
Aquarius (all the ingredients of a beautiful friendship)
Gemini (both flippin' high-spirted)
Might be Ok with... Scorpio, Sagittarius
50/50 chance with... Taurus, Pisces
No bloomin' chance with... Capricorn, Cancer

Gem stone Opal

Bubblegum Crew
who are Librans

Veggie

Old Git

Scorpio 23rd October - 22nd November

A Scorpio likes to keep secrets
they do it as a matter of course
No one ever knows what they're thinking
they're a proper bloomin' dark horse!

If you're a Scorpio, then this means you are a water sign.
So your characteristics include being a bit secretive
(you never let on who you're going out with), passionate
about things (a right nutter sometimes), but you can
be a little obsessive (especially about pop groups).

Perfect Boy / Girlfriend
Pisces (lots of emotional support going on here)
Cancer (get along so well as an item)
Might be Ok with... Scorpio, Virgo
50/50 chance with... Aries, Gemini
No bloomin' chance with... Aquarius, Taurus, Leo, Scorpio

Gem stone Topaz

Bubblegum Crew
who are Scorpios

Waaaaaaaaaaaa

Slap Head

Bonce Wax

Flippin' Mental

Sagittarius 23rd November – 20th December

A Sagittarius is ever optimistic
always looking on the bright side
But they're blunt with their true opinions
and the truth they never can hide!

If you're a Sagittarian, then this means you are a fire sign.
So your characteristics include being ever so optimistic
(the glass of pop is half full not half empty), always happy
(grinning like a bloomin' Cheshire moggy) but you can
be a little blunt, (what an awful dress you've got on).

Perfect Boy/Girlfriend
Aries (both philosophical)
Leo (love to travel together)
Might be Ok with... Scorpio, Capricorn
50/50 chance with... Taurus, Cancer
No bloomin' chance with... Pisces, Gemini, Virgo

Gem stone Turquoise

Bubblegum Crew
who are Sagittarians

Blonde Bombshell

Scrumptious Bum

Capricorn 21st December – 19th January

A Capricorn is so organised
and choc full of ambition
They go after what they want
on a big bad flippin' mission!

If you're a Capricorn, then you are an Earth sign.
This means that you are very organised (just look
at your bedroom) and full of ambition (you will
be a pop star), although you can overwork
yourself (a proper swot!).

Perfect Boy/Girlfriend
Virgo (made for each other)
Taurus (share the same dreams!)
Might be Ok with... Pisces, Scorpio
50/50 chance with... Gemini, Leo, Capricorn
No bloomin' chance with... Aries, Cancer, Libra

Gem stone Onyx

Bubblegum Crew
who are Capricorns

Mr Muscles

Happenin'
Babe

Aquarius 20th January – 18th February

Aquarians are so independent
they need no one – that's true
But they're pals with most people
and can be good friends too!

If you're an Aquarian, then this means you are an air sign.
So your characteristics include being fiercely independent
(you're the one who will go the pictures alone), a bit of a
thinker (a proper deep one), but you can sometimes appear
aloof (no thank you, it's not my type).

Perfect Boy/Girlfriend
Gemini (both value independence)
Libra (both have a few really close pals)
Might be Ok with... Pisces, Aries, Sagittarius
50/50 chance with... Cancer, Virgo
No bloomin' chance with... Taurus, Leo, Scorpio

Gem stone Amethyst

Bubblegum Crew
who are Aquarians

Curry
Monster

Disco
Diva

Drama
Queen

Pisces 19th February – 20th March

Pisceans are really big softees
they are sensitive and kind
A more caring, gentle person
you will never find!

If you're an Piscean, then this means you are a water sign.
So your characteristics include being compassionate
(you'd adopt a million cats if you could), being sensitive
(you blub at the drop of a hat), although you can tend
to be a bit unfocused at times (nutty as a fruitcake!).

Perfect Boy / Girlfriend
Cancer (utterly devoted)
Scorpio (totally in love)
Might be Ok with... Taurus, Aries, Capricorn, Aquarius
50/50 chance with... Leo, Libra
No bloomin' chance with... Gemini, Virgo

Gem stone Aquamarine

Bubblegum Crew
who are Pisceans

Sun Junkie

Dancing
Queen

chatterbox's cheesy chat up lines

Hey, don't we go to different schools together?

If I could rearrange the alphabet,
I'd put U and I together.

-Did it hurt?
-What?
-When you fell from heaven.

Do you have a ten pence piece? Because my mum
told me to call her when I fell in love.

Can beauty be spelt without U in it?

-Now I understand why the sky has been grey all day!
-Why
-Because all the blue is in your eyes! - yeuch!

Nice to meet you, I'm (your name) and you are...gorgeous!

You know, you might be asked to leave soon. You're making the other girls/boys look really bad.

I've had a really bad day. I love to see a nice girl/boy smile. Could you help me out?

The only thing your eyes haven't told me is your name.

If I follow you home, will you keep me?

Can gorgeous be spelt without U in it?

1

Yep, a proper **Hug** Monster!

2

You're a bit loopy but ever so nice

3

Cool as a cucumber

How to be a... Secret Admirer

Having a Secret Admirer is really cool – it's really nice to know that someone mysterious thinks you're really spesh. Being someone's secret admirer is also cool 'cos you can admire them from a distance without anyone knowing. The bestest way to let someone know you think they're proper gorgeous is to send them a Valentine's Day card. Don't sign it – just put a big question mark in it and keep 'em guessing. However, remember not to blush when you walk past them because 'Beacon Cheeks' are a proper giveaway especially on Valentine's Day. If you feel your cheeks starting to glow, head for some fresh air and hope that the Spesh person doesn't rumble you as their Secret Admirer.

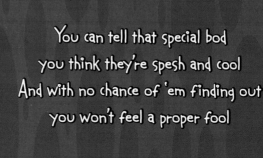

You can tell that special bod
you think they're spesh and cool
And with no chance of 'em finding out
you won't feel a proper fool

10 Disco Diva's Top Ten Smoochies

True - Spandau Ballet
Love me Tender - Elvis
How Deep is your Love - The Bee Gees
Save a Prayer - Duran Duran
I Just Called to Say 'I Love You' - Stevie Wonder
Yesterday Once More - The Carpenters
Groovy Kind of Love - The Mindbenders
Wonderful World - Sam Cooke
Power of Love - Frankie goes to Hollywood
Unchained Melody - The Righteous Brothers

10 Funk Soul Brother's Big Love Anthems

Total Eclipse of the Heart - Bonnie Tyler
Love is in the Air - John Paul Young
Be my Baby - The Ronnettes
It's not Unusual - Tom Jones
Love Me Do - The Beatles
Take a Chance on Me - ABBA
I Lost my Heart to a Starship Trooper - Hot Gossip and Sarah Brightman
You're the One that I want - John Travolta and Olivia Newton-John
Don't Go Breaking my Heart - Elton John and Kiki Dee
I Feel Love - Donna Summer

How many do you know?

ARE YOU IN LUV?

When some people want to fall in love
they wish upon a star
Check out this groovy quiz
to see if you really are

 1

When you see that special person,
your heart goes...?

A. Slightly faster
B. Twice as fast
C. A flippin' million times a second

 2

In your personalised dictionary
under love, what can you see?

A. A picture of a heart
B. A picture of a heart with your name
and a question mark underneath
C. A picture of your spesh person

3

Unaware of your feelings a new friend of
yours says your spesh person is a proper
gorgepot. Do you go...?

A. Yes, they're quite nice, aren't they?
B. Red with embarassment
C. Green with envy

 4

That special person smiles at you
when you pass them in the corridor.
Do you...

A. Pass a smile back
B. Pass a smile back and go bright red
C. Pass out

 5

Your spesh bod is very insistent and
asks you out to the movies. You say...

A. Oh, be patient will you, I'll look in
my diary
B. Ok. Be at my house at six
C. Oh, be still, my beating heart

 6

How many cards are you going to send
your special person on Valentine's Day?

A. One
B. One hundred
C. One million

7 If you were on a desert island,
what three things would you take...?

A. Chocolate, a good book and a radio
B. Chocolate, a mobile phone and
a radio
C. Chocolate, your spesh bod and
some wings ('cos you'd be in heaven)

8 It's the last dance at the party and it's a slow one.
That spesh bod comes and asks you to dance. Do you...?

A. Drag them to one side and tell them
not to embarass you
B. Drag them to a corner of the dance floor
hoping nobody notices too much
C. Drag them to the middle of the dance floor before
they've finished asking you, drawing as much attention
to the two of you as is humanly possible

9 Someone has carved your name in a big heart
on a tree. What do you do...?

A. Get annoyed because you don't know who it is
B. Get embarassed because it's secretly flattering
C. Get down there and add the name of your spesh bod

10 You get a big bunch of flowers on your
birthday. Do you...?

A. Start guessing who they're from
B. Start ringing around to find out
who sent them
C. Start plucking the petals off saying,
'He loves me, he loves me not.'

Looks like Hunny Bunny's
got the answers...

So... are you in Lurve?

Mostly A

Soz, no passion here I'm afraid. You are not in love at the moment, but who knows what's around the corner.

Mostly B

Ooooh, you're getting there but not quite yet. There's a fifty-fifty chance that you'll fall head over heels in the next few weeks. So watch out, lurve might be coming to your part of town very soon indeed.

Mostly C

No doubt about it you've gone big time. You are in love. Enjoy it!

Still not sure? Well, here's Love Docta with the sauce on the symptoms...

Tummy
Absolutely full of butterflies

Feet
Feel like they're walking on air

Hands
Shake in their presence — making having a cup of tea very difficult

Legs
Turn to Jelly at the mention of their name

Heartbeat
A million times a minute

Lips
Can't help saying the daftest things

Knees
Knock together proper fast

BOOM
BOOM
BOOM

Scrambled Brains
All messed up and can't think about anything but the one you love

Beacon Cheeks
Bright red and glowing each time you speak to that spesh person

s	l	a	h	j	d	v	e	r	o	s	m
n	u	w	h	o	t	l	i	p	s	d	n
p	s	w	s	s	m	d	j	i	m	i	r
i	h	s	e	p	e	c	k	k	w	h	e
o	l	n	w	b	c	t	s	i	a	v	k
u	i	o	t	u	a	s	n	s	a	v	c
t	p	g	k	f	i	y	x	s	a	h	a
r	s	s	g	k	r	v	j	y	n	n	m
l	k	i	p	s	m	o	o	c	h	c	s
p	b	o	x	n	q	p	o	x	y	t	n
o	t	m	l	i	p	b	u	m	p	s	l
o	n	m	k	j	h	l	t	u	l	j	k
r	s	r	e	g	g	o	n	s	t	o	h

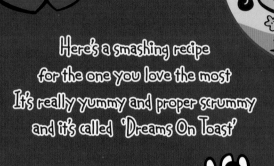

Here's a smashing recipe
for the one you love the most
It's really yummy and proper scrummy
and it's called 'Dreams On Toast'

Impress your special bod
with this simple but scrummy
love recipe. It's tons of fun
and it's easy peasy to make.

Ingredients

2 slices of bread
1 tin of beans
Butter or margarine

Method

Pop the bread in a toaster or under a grill
for one minute or until golden brown.
Then remove and allow to cool.
Once cool, cut out two heart shapes from the
toast. Butter the shapes and place on a plate.
Open beans and heat gently for one minute.
Spread the beans onto the heart shapes and serve.

Tell the recipient that each baked bean represents
a dream and a wish shared with them. Enjoy!

A RECIPE FOR LURVE

If you want a proper treat
and really want to impress
Just follow these simple instructions
and then clear up the mess

Krispy Love Bombs are just bursting
with krazy flavour and go down a
flippin' treat. Impress the whole world
with your cookin' skills.

Ingredients

50g White Cooking Chocolate
Three drops of red food colouring
A cup of Rice Krispies
Rice paper cake cups

Method

Heat the choc in a small pan until fluid (gloopy).
Add the food colouring. Mix in the Rice Krispies
then spoon out into individual cake cups. Put in fridge to cool.

Tell whoever you give a cake to that twenty minutes after
eating they will be irresistible to anyone near.

And don't forget to wash up!

BE A BARD

Want to send that certain scrummy someone a high voltage Valentine's verse Bubblegum style? You can crank out umpteen or more rinky dinky l'il lurve poems with this funky four line poem writer. It's easy!

Simply pick one line from each box, 1 to 4 in order and you've cracked it. See, faster than a very fast thing.

1

You really are fantastic

Wow you're just so flippin' spesh

I luv you tons and tons

You're a proper gorgepot

2

You're mental through and through

Without you I'd be blue

As soon as I saw you I knew

The sexiest ever it's true

You're really great, a proper mate

My heart you rule you crazy fool

It's easy to see and I'm sure you'll agree

You're scrummy you are

my Valentine's star

I love you I flippin' well do!

I fancy the pants off you!

You're a big love monster too!

Let's do some love kung fu!

see ya!

Ta-ra for now, we hope you thought
our guide to lurve was bliss
So go on out into the world
and give everyone a kiss!